G000036628

Introduction

Welcome to **The Number Crew**, a series designed to meet the numeracy needs of 5 to 7 year olds. The programmes are grouped in units by year and are devised to support and inspire the teaching and learning of numeracy through 3-D animated stories, 2-D animated songs, presenter-led studio sequences and real-life images.

Each programme in this animated puppet soap opera has a specific mathematical focus, closely related to the content of the National Numeracy Framework, which schools in England will be expected to follow from September 1999. (The programmes will be equally applicable to the teaching of mathematics to infants in Wales, Northern Ireland and Scotland.) The thirty programmes for each infant year-group are divided into three units, each of ten 10-minute programmes, reflecting three key strands of the Framework: 'Numbers and the Number System', 'Calculations' and 'Solving Problems'.

The programmes (and associated support materials) can be used as a lively, integral part of the Mathematics lesson. By providing animated stories, songs, graphics and real-life images, they are excellent foci for whole-class teaching.

At the beginning of each programme, the action takes place on board a 'luxury' cruise ship, the SS *Mathematical*, where the human Number Crew look after the needs of 20 charming but demanding animal passengers. In each episode, as the ship's journey unfolds, the Number Crew encounter a mathematical problem that needs to be solved. Viewers are encouraged to join with the Number Crew in identifying the mathematical concept at the heart of the problem, and developing the mental strategies and skills required to solve it.

This Teachers' Guide for the unit **Solving Problems** for 5 to 6 year olds, together with the other resource material for the series, has been specially written to enhance the programmes and make them easy to use within all forms of classroom organisation. It provides an outline of the programmes and suggestions for activities before, during and after viewing. More information about **The Number Crew** and in particular the unit **Solving Problems** is given on the following pages. Also included are the words and music to the songs, which have been written specially for the programmes.

I hope that you find the programmes helpful as well as enjoyable. I would be extremely pleased to receive any comments, suggestions and examples of children's work. Please send any correspondence to:

Liz Meenan
Education Officer
Channel 4 Schools
PO Box 100
Warwick CV34 6TZ

contents

Subtitles
This Channel 4 Schools series is subtitled in Teletext for the deaf and hearing-impaired.

About The Number Crew

Underlying ideas and aims

The programmes and resources have been designed to:

- give a focused and stimulating selection of ideas and starting points for numeracy work in the classroom;

- support direct teaching and interactive oral work with the whole class;

- emphasise mental calculation;

- develop children's understanding and use of mathematical vocabulary;

- encourage discussion of ways to tackle problems;

- suggest cross-curricular links, especially with English, music and PE;

- engage, stimulate and challenge children and encourage them to become more independent and confident in their numeracy work;

- provide teachers with a flexible set of resources which can be used alongside any infant maths scheme.

Structure

The series of 60 programmes is divided into three sets of ten 10-minute programme units for each of the two year-groups in the 5 to 7 age range. The units reflect three key areas of the National Numeracy Framework:

Numbers and the Number System

- counting
- properties of numbers and number sequences
- place value and ordering (including reading and writing numbers)
- estimating and rounding
- introduction to fractions and decimals

Calculations

- understanding number operations
- instant mental recall of number facts
- mental calculation strategies for deriving new facts from facts known already
- pencil-and-paper methods
- checking that results of calculations are reasonable

Solving Problems

- making decisions: deciding which operation and method of calculation to use (mental, partly mental and partly pencil-and-paper, pencil-and-paper, calculator, and so on)
- reasoning about numbers and making general statements
- solving problems involving numbers in familiar contexts such as: everyday life; money; measurement, including choosing units and scales; collecting, presenting and interpreting numerical data

The programme units are based on the National Numeracy Framework (which is based on the Mathematics National Curriculum for England and Wales), but all the programmes are equally applicable to the mathematics curricula of Scotland and Northern Ireland.

The first three units of **The Number Crew** for 5 to 6 year olds are first broadcast in 1998/99. The other three units for 6 to 7 year olds are first broadcast in 1999/2000.

Programme format

- Each programme concentrates on a single mathematical idea in a pupil-friendly way. See the next page for details of the programmes in this unit.

- Each programme ends with a question or activity for the teacher to explore after viewing.

- Each programme features a combination of various elements:

- An episode from a **3-D animated soap opera** which is set on board the 'luxury' cruise ship SS *Mathematical*, where the human Number Crew (Fiz, Flo, Bradley, Baby Bunting and their parents Ted and Mirabelle) look after the needs of 20 charming but demanding animal passengers. In each episode, the Number Crew encounter a problem which can only be solved by the application of mathematical knowledge and skills. Viewers are encouraged to help the Number Crew identify the concept at the heart of the problem, develop strategies and skills to solve it, and then sail on into untroubled waters.

- One or two **songs** about the mathematics on which the programme is focused. Songs can be an infectious form of 'rote learning'. Through them children can learn the mathematical facts by heart; or explore the rule or principle behind the programme. The songs are fun to hear and fun to sing.

- **2-D animation** used to illustrate the songs or calculations, showing the maths within each programme in an entertaining way. Being visible on screen the maths become clear, explicit and memorable.

- **Real-life examples** in which number knowledge and skills are acquired and applied. These demonstrate the connection between maths and life, and include home, school, parks, shops and other locations. These sequences are stylish, set to music, and relevant to children.

- **'Living numbers'**: children who 'become' numbers, number sequences and calculations and 'act out' the maths. The 'living numbers' help make the maths clearer and fun, and illustrate links between maths and PE games. They also show that children can experience maths with their whole body as well as their minds.

- **Studio sequences** in a spectacular seaside set. These link all the other elements together. The presenter, Matthew Lyons, leads the viewers through the maths. He uses song, demonstration and explanation to make the maths clear and direct.

Different parts of the set illustrate different types of mathematical learning. For example, the number lines children have in the classroom are reflected in our Number Line – but on a grand scale, like a 'world of numbers' theme park. As Matthew drives up and down the Line in his Number Car, he explores the number system in exactly the way a teacher might – but using all the resources of television at his disposal. Similarly, the Quiz Set is where Matthew, playing 'What's That Number?', encourages the development of the quick mental skills that modern maths teaching expects of children.

Using the programmes

We recommend that you record the programmes to make the best use of them. You can then preview them and decide how best they could support your teaching. Pre-recording the programmes not only gives greater flexibility in deciding when to watch, but allows for a wider range of teaching styles. The video can be paused at key points and your pupils can discuss what's happening on screen, predict what's going to happen and answer any questions posed. You can also review particular aspects of programmes as often as you like. Most importantly, the programmes can become part of your library of resources to support numeracy work.

The ideal way to use the series is to record the programmes and then:

- preview each programme and decide on the best time to view with the class;

- before viewing a programme, revise and talk about the ideas within it;

- view the programme, pausing where appropriate and encouraging discussion;

- have some discussion, and then re-show the programme without pausing;

- follow up with related activities.

The Mathematics Lesson

For those teachers following the National Numeracy Framework, a typical lesson (about 50 minutes) will be structured like this:

- Oral work and mental calculation work with the whole class.

- The main teaching activity with the whole class, groups, pairs or targeted individuals.

- A plenary session with the whole class to round off the lesson.

The programmes and support materials fit easily into this lesson structure. These resources will help teachers meet the demands of the Framework.

- At the beginning of the lesson, before viewing, the teacher could take some of the ideas and suggestions in this Teachers' Guide and use them for preliminary mental arithmetic exercises (about 10 minutes' work).

- Next the class could view one whole programme. Afterwards, with the help of the activities in the Teachers' Guide and Activity Book, explore and discuss the concept that the programme illustrates (about 30 minutes' work).

- The lesson can be brought to an end with a whole-class discussion so the pupils can give their opinions on the programme and activities, review the mathematics they have seen, heard and done, and take stock for the next maths session (about 10 minutes' work).

The Number Crew is ideal for teaching numeracy. You'll also find uses for it in PE, music and English. You can even use it in drama: get your children to be Bradley, Flo, Fiz, tiger, monkey, and so on. It brings humour and colour into teaching and learning mathematics. And each story actively engages viewers, appealing to their hearts and minds.

Solving Problems

There are ten programmes in **Solving Problems** for 5 to 6 year olds.

1 **The Roller Coaster 1** – Understanding and using the vocabulary related to measuring and solving length problems.

2 **The Roller Coaster 2** – Understanding and using the vocabulary related to measuring and solving mass problems.

3 **Drinks in the Sun** – Understanding and using the vocabulary related to measuring and solving capacity problems.

4 **The Funfair** – Recognising coins and their equivalent money values; solving money problems.

5 **More Fun at the Fair** – Choosing the appropriate number operations to solve number problems.

6 **The Treasure Hunt** – Solving numerical problems, recognising simple patterns or relationships, generalising and making predictions.

7 **It's Yo-Yo Time** – Understanding and using the vocabulary related to time and units of time.

8 **Do it for Charity** – Reading the time from clocks and solving time problems.

9 **Sports Day** – Collecting and recording numerical data.

10 **The Number Crew Awards** – Collecting, recording, discussing and making predictions from numerical data.

Who's in the series

Mirabelle made her money and her mistakes back in her twenties as a rock star. Wanting to make up for lost time, she needed a new direction in life. Should she become an infant teacher, or transport an assorted collection of animals round the world? The latter seemed the easier option, and Mirabelle chartered an elegant but faded liner. Her eyes are now firmly on the horizon, which leaves her children with rather more to do than the average 6 year old – which is probably no bad thing.

Ted for many years watched his idol Mirabelle from the wings as one of her roadies. When she left showbiz behind, he couldn't believe his luck when she asked him to join her on her voyage into a new life. They adopted Fiz, Bradley and Flo, and their mutual joy was sealed (though possibly short-lived) when Baby Bunting was born. Ted is now delighted to be First Mate in the round-the-world voyage of the SS *Mathematical*, and to lend his steady determination to Mirabelle's inspiration.

Fiz is full of energy, never daunted, least of all by being in a wheelchair. 'Let's do it!' is her motto, and action usually comes before thought. She is seldom still, occasionally at loggerheads with Bradley, but always ready to give things a go with a full heart and turbo-powered wheelchair spin.

Bradley is one of life's careful characters. He likes to keep things under control, and sometimes clutches his clipboard to himself as another child might cuddle a teddy. He rather expects disaster, and very often rightly. 'It's all going wrong' is his usual plaintive cry.

Flo is younger than Fiz and Bradley, and a lot calmer than either of them. 'Let's think about it' is what she often advises. She is sensitive as well as being sensible. She is the only one who can reliably understand what the animals are talking about.

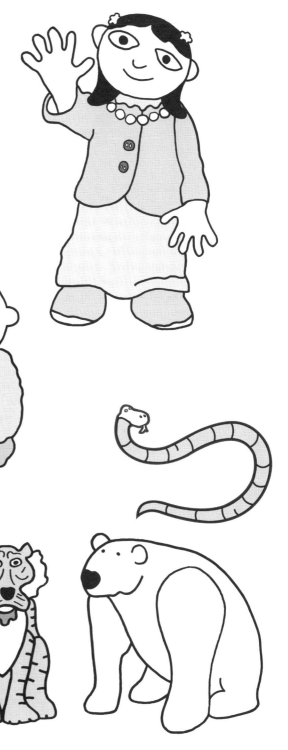

Baby Bunting turns up when least expected. He has a way of causing and even enjoying a crisis, and is fortunately indestructible. Renowned and named for his flags-of-all-nations underwear, he is both a trial and a delight to the rest of his family.

The **twenty animal passengers** are an interesting mix. The elephant, the rhino, the moose, the lion, the tiger, the zebra, the crocodile, the buffalo, the giraffe, the penguin, the ostrich, the turtle, the polar bear, the snake, the kangaroo, the hippo, the monkey, the gorilla, the camel and the panda are a cheerful but demanding group of passengers, whose animal urges – for food, fun and entertainment – pose endless mathematical problems for the Number Crew.

Matthew Lyons is our guide to the shipboard goings-on. Back on shore he spends his time cheerfully on the beach, ready to dispense mathematical toys and knowledge to anyone who's interested. With his cuddly numbers, his spectacular Number Line, his Number Car, and his quizmaster's hat, he'll sing, dance, explain, live, breathe and teach maths.

1 | The Roller Coaster 1

Programme outline

None of the animal passengers wants Bradley's bananas – except the monkey. The others are far too busy having fun 'roller booting'. As a joke, Bradley suggests the next thing the animals might want is a roller coaster; Fiz and the animals take him seriously and think that it is a brilliant idea. The presenter explains what a roller coaster is, and wonders how the Number Crew could build one. Fiz decides she could pull the cars with her wheelchair, if Ted could make the track and Bradley and Flo make the cars. They all set to work.

Flo makes a car which is very beautiful but much too small. Bradley's car is far too large. The children realise that to make sure the cars are the right size, they need to measure the animals. Seeing the monkey hold up the bananas against himself gives Bradley the idea of measuring the animals in bananas.

After a 'real world' sequence showing many things of different sizes, Matthew hosts a quiz show called 'Compare the Pair'. He ends the programme by suggesting that viewers could try a similar quiz show in the classroom. The final challenge is to find out how tall their teacher is – using pencils or, possibly, bananas.

Learning outcomes

Children should gain experience of:

- the use of vocabulary relating to measuring length;

- comparing lengths;

- solving length problems.

Vocabulary

measure	*long/short*
length	*high/low*
width	*wide/narrow*
height	*longer/shorter*
depth	*taller/shorter*
opposites	*higher/lower*

Before viewing

Talk to the children about size. Young children are often intrigued by the giants and tiny people in traditional stories. Ask questions like: What do we mean by 'big' or 'little'? Some children have an intuitive feel for the relative meaning of the words. Point out that, in order to be more accurate about describing size, they need to think about particular aspects, like length, height and width.

While viewing

► Stop the tape when Matthew asks viewers 'What needs to be done to Flo's car before the moose could ride in it?'

► Encourage the children to join in 'It Needs To Be Longer' and the title song (see pages 28 and 30).

Follow-up activities

Recap

Talk through the programme with the children. Encourage them to use other words for 'big' and 'little' as they talk about how the Number Crew solved the problem of the roller coaster.

Repeat the song 'It Needs To Be Longer'.

End-of-programme problem

This problem could lead to an interesting comparison of heights for the whole class. Ask the children to bring in their teddy bears and measure them. Show the children how to measure objects longer than one unit length by repeating the chosen unit so that there is no overlap or gap.

Take up Matthew's idea of a 'Compare the Pair' quiz by collecting suitable objects such as ribbons, straws, sticks and pencils and putting them in a 'feely bag'. The bag is passed round as the children sit in a ring. Choose children to take out two of the objects and say something about their relative size. Give points to the children who can make more than one comparison.

Measuring linked to other subjects

Ideally work on measures should always be connected with work in other subject areas: for example, in science or technology where the children need to measure appropriately in order to solve problems.

The language we use for comparing lengths can be emphasised during a PE session. An interesting problem to pose the class is: 'How far can you reach?'

Appropriate units

Ask the children to suggest things in the classroom that could be used for measuring. What would they use to measure a table, a book, or a tray?

Work could be extended into measuring using appropriate parts of the body such as feet, fingers or hands. Tell the class these measurements are very useful for a rough measure. Spend some time having the children measure using strides or spans and compare the different results that they get. This leads to the recognition of the need for us all to agree on a standard measure. The traditional story of the Queen's Bed is a good illustration of how important it is when we measure in feet that the feet are the same size. See page 31 for a version of the story, called 'The King's Bed'.

The Roller Coaster 2

Programme outline

The Number Crew and passengers are having a great time on the roller coaster until Fiz's wheelchair breaks down. Ted says the motor of the wheelchair is getting too hot, as she's been pulling too much mass: that is, too many passengers. Matthew explains what 'mass' means. Fiz accepts Ted's warning that the wheelchair will break down again if she pulls anything heavier than the elephant. The Number Crew feel certain that the elephant must be the heaviest of the passengers, but decide to check following Ted's suggestion to use a see-saw.

The elephant gets bored sitting on one end of the see-saw so the presenter shows how the elephant can be replaced by blocks. The Number Crew find out that several animals together weigh less than the elephant, so they could have a ride on the roller coaster together. After a 'real life' montage of things sold by weight, Matthew offers several suggestions for further weighing activities.

Learning outcomes

Children should gain experience of:

● the vocabulary related to comparing and measuring weight or mass;

● solving problems involving weight or mass.

Vocabulary

mass	*heaviest*
weight	*light*
weighs	*lighter*
balances	*lightest*
heavy	*scales*
heavier	*balance*

Before viewing

▶ Children need to be aware of the words 'mass' and 'weight'. 'Mass' is the correct scientific term but 'weight' is more commonly used, certainly in general conversation. (The amount of matter in an object is called its mass. Weight is a measure of the force which the Earth exerts on a body. So the mass of an object never changes, but the weight can depend on how far it is from the Earth's surface.)

▶ Many children require a great deal of experience to dissociate the concept of weight (mass) from size. Ask questions like: Are large things always heavier than small things? What large things can be light? What small things can be heavy?

While viewing

▶ Stop the tape when Flo asks if there is any way they could manage without the elephant. Ask the children if they can offer any solutions to the problem.

▶ Encourage the children to join in the 'Mass Mass' and title songs (see pages 27 and 30).

Follow-up activities

Recap

Talk through the programme with the children and ask them to describe what they have seen and heard.

Sing the 'Mass Mass' song again.

End-of-programme problem

Matthew raises several possibilities which you could choose to follow up. Demonstrate to the class how to use a balance to find out answers to two of Matthew's problems. The children could then work on similar problems in pairs. Put out a selection of 'units' for weighing. These could include blocks, marbles, weights, cubes, beads, and so on. Select some objects to be weighed (a toy, a tennis ball, a book, for example). Then set problems like: How many blocks do your toys weigh? How many marbles weigh the same as a tennis ball?

You will need to organise your class according to the number of balances you have available.

The third problem – 'How many children weigh the same as a teacher?' – needs to be tackled differently. If you don't want to go into standard measures by using bathroom scales, you could arrange for a visit to the local park to use the see-saw, if you don't have one available in school.

Balancing in other subjects

PE lessons could include some discussion and opportunities for the children to balance while standing on their toes, on one leg, and so on.

Cooking also provides opportunities for the children to use a balance for a definite purpose.

Traditional recipe for six queen cakes

Ingredients:

One egg and the weight of an egg in butter, sugar and self-raising flour.

Method:

Cream the butter and sugar, add the egg and beat well.

Stir in the sifted flour.

Add a little milk if the mixture is too stiff.

Divide equally between nine bun tins and cook in a moderate oven for 10 to 12 minutes.

Sorting by weight

Make a collection of objects which could be sorted according to weight. Perhaps a bag of sugar could be used for comparison. First demonstrate to the whole class by holding the objects in your hands and then by balancing. Allow the children to choose different objects to compare. More able children are probably aware of the 'kilo' and they could move into weighing with standard weights.

Mobiles

If you have enough adult help, the children could be encouraged to make a simple mobile, using a wire coat hanger and a selection of mathematical shapes or animal shapes made from card or paper which they need to balance by moving them nearer or further away from the centre.

3 Drinks in the Sun

Programme outline

Ted and Mirabelle hope the children are looking after the animals properly in the heat by making sure they drink lots of water. However, the animals don't want to drink as much water as they should. The children decide to make more interesting containers to 'tempt' them. Bradley makes a tall thin one, Fiz makes a large shallow one and Flo makes a middle-sized one decorated with flowers. The animal passengers like the new containers and wonder which holds the most water. Matthew shows how to compare the capacity of the containers by pouring from one to the other. The passengers see that Bradley's container holds the same amount as Fiz's container, and, by using a jug, they are able to check that Fiz's container holds the same as Flo's.

Matthew then challenges the viewers to estimate how many glasses of orange juice he can get out of a carton, and ends the programme by asking viewers to estimate how much they drink during a day.

Learning outcomes

Children should gain experience of:

● the vocabulary related to measuring capacity;

● estimating quantities;

● solving problems related to capacity.

Vocabulary

full	*tall*
empty	*thin*
capacity	*large*
holds	*shallow*
container	

Before viewing

The programme will be most effective for children who have had practical experience of pouring water, sand, and so on, into and from a variety of containers. Links could be made to work in science about the needs of animals, or work on the topic 'ourselves' and the need for all animals to have adequate amounts of water to drink.

▶ Check on vocabulary by asking questions like: What is meant by 'full' and 'empty'? What is the difference between half-full and half-empty?

While viewing

▶ Stop the tape when Matthew asks whether viewers can suggest how Bradley and Flo could find out which container holds most.

▶ Encourage the children to join in singing 'Drink Drink' and the title song (see pages 26 and 30).

Follow-up activities

Recap

Let the children talk about the programme. Ask them if they were surprised that the containers made by the Number Crew all held the same amount of water. Ask if they can always tell whether one container holds more than another one just by looking at them.

Sing the 'Drink Drink' song again.

End-of-programme problem

Matthew's question about how much viewers drink during a day could be a good starting point for work on data handling. If the day in question is a school day, the results could be made into a graph. This could be compared later with a survey of a day during the weekend. This would obviously need the co-operation of parents. But it would be a valuable opportunity for the children to make estimations and measurements in a meaningful context and encourage some school-home links at the same time.

Comparing and ordering

Other opportunities for meaningful measurements arise in cooking and baking when recipes use the words 'cupful' and 'spoonful'. Using and comparing small cups, teapots, jugs and so on from the house corner or doll's house can be very useful for some children. If appropriate, you could encourage the children to estimate the capacity of some of the containers before measuring. However, before children can really estimate, they need lots of practical experience.

You could start a collection of containers of different shapes and sizes which the children, working in pairs, could order according to capacity. Fine sand or rice could be used instead of water. You could ask the children when it would be sensible to measure: in spoonfuls; in egg cups; in cups; in jugs.

Cooking

This can offer opportunities for using measures based on capacity. American recipes particularly seem to favour using 'cupfuls' and 'spoonfuls'.

Recipe for play dough

Ingredients:

2 cups plain flour

1 cup salt

2 cups cold water

4 tablespoons cooking oil

4 teaspoons cream of tartar

a few drops of food colouring

Method:

Put all the ingredients into a pan.

Heat gently and mix together. It is ready when the dough pulls away from the side.

4 The Funfair

Programme outline

The animals are getting bored so Fiz suggests having a funfair. Mirabelle says they could provide a free funfair, but it would be more like a real funfair if the passengers could have some money. Ted agrees to make some money for them to use and Mirabelle tells the children that they will have to teach the animals the value of the different coins. Matthew agrees that it's no good the animals having money if they don't know what it's worth. The animals pay attention to the lecture about the value of the coins, but Flo thinks they are still a little bit confused. Fiz suggests a song which would help the animals to understand. The presenter introduces a sequence illustrating how we use money in 'real life' situations.

At the funfair the animal passengers have a good time trying out their skills. Bradley shows the buffalo how to play the penny game. Flo shows the ostrich how to play darts, and the tiger and the monkey win at bingo. At darts, the ostrich wins a fluffy toy which turns out to be Baby Bunting in disguise.

Matthew ends the programme by suggesting the viewers make some funfair stalls – just like the Number Crew.

Learning outcomes

Children should gain experience of:

● recognising coins;

● equivalent money values;

● solving simple money problems.

Vocabulary

money	*cost*
coin	*price*
pence	*change*
penny	*how much?*

Before viewing

The programme will be most effective for children who have had some experience of recognising 1p, 2p, 5p and 10p coins, and some experience of adding mentally to 10.

▶ Talk to the children about going to a funfair and how they like to spend their money. Which are the most expensive activities? Which are the cheapest?

While viewing

▶ Stop the tape when Mirabelle tells the crew they have to explain the value of the coins to the animals. Ask the children if they could do it. Help them to describe some of the coins they know, giving them words like 'silver', 'copper', and so on.

▶ Encourage them to sing along with 'One And Two' and the title song (see pages 28 and 30).

Follow-up activities

Recap

Talk through the programme with the children and ask them to think about what they have seen and heard.

Sing the song 'One And Two' again.

Matthew's problems

Remind the children about some of the problems Matthew raised. Ask, if they were running the 'Double Your Money' stall, could they double 2 pence? Or double 5 pence? Or what about 10 pence? What if they were running the bingo stall and it was 5 pence a go, could they work out how much money they would get from three customers?

If they were running the darts stall, could they add up the scores? Flo added three numbers in her head – 'four add three add two'. Can the children?

Give the children more oral problems of this kind, using your knowledge of the class to target individual children with problems at appropriate levels.

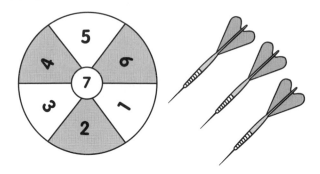

Make a funfair, shop or café

Allow the children to make their own funfair in the classroom by preparing several board games which the children can play in groups or pairs. Playing games like these helps children to become more fluent in their knowledge of the number bonds introduced in previous programmes.

If you think a funfair would not be feasible, set up a shop or café in the home corner and arrange for children to buy and sell things. Encourage them to work out mentally the cost of items they buy, or meals they order.

Price all the items at less than 10p and allow each 'shopper' only 10p to spend. After the children have gained experience of 'shopping', make up mental problems with the class. For example: 'Laura spent 4p. What's her change from 10p?' 'Liam spent 5p, 3p and 1p. How much did he spend altogether? What is his change from 10p?'

5 | More Fun at the Fair

Programme outline

The children want to have a go on the sidestalls of the funfair. Mirabelle says they can have 20p each, but they have to keep track of what they spend. Matthew introduces the 20p piece and the different plans the children have. Bradley decides to make a list of everything he spends; Fiz will take away in her head every time she spends something; and Flo wants to visit all the stalls so she will share out her money equally.

The animal passengers are not great at running the stalls, but the Number Crew enjoy themselves. All their strategies work. Matthew sings the song 'There's More Than One Way of Solving a Problem' and introduces the quiz 'Solve That Problem'. He leaves the viewers with a challenge to make up some problems of their own.

Learning outcomes

Children should gain experience of:

● equivalent values of 20p;

● choosing the appropriate operation to solve a problem.

Vocabulary

add	*how many more to make ... ?*
sum	*makes*
total	*leaves*
altogether	*equals*
take	*share*
take away	*once, twice, three times ...*
subtract	*double*

Before viewing

The programme will be most appropriate for children who can recognise 1p, 2p, 5p and 10p coins and have had experience of working out simple problems mentally.

▶ Talk to the children about spending money and how they calculate how much they have to spend when they go to the shop or visit a funfair.

While viewing

▶ Encourage the children to sing along with 'There's More Than One Way Of Solving A Problem' and the title song (see pages 27 and 30).

▶ Stop the tape when Matthew presents the 'Solve That Problem' quiz. Ask the children for their solutions.

Follow-up activities

Recap

Allow time for the children to reflect on what they have seen and heard. Spend some time talking about how the three children of the Number Crew spent their 20 pence. Ask if anyone could come and write up the equivalent number sentences on the board or flip chart.

Sing the song 'There's More Than One Way Of Solving A Problem' again.

'Show me' activities

After spending some time talking through several problems with the whole class, you could give the children smaller, individual sets of cards and play 'show me' activities. Present some simple single-operation problems orally and, instead of always asking for the children to show you the answer, ask them to show you the operation card which tells you how they worked out the answer. If appropriate, ask the children to write down the number sentences.

End-of-programme problem

Talk about the problem with the children. The problem is: 'If candy floss costs 5p and a toffee apple costs 10p, in how many ways can you spend 20p?' Encourage the children to consider different ways of working out the answer, using mental skills they are confident with. Give them some time to work out as many ways as they can. Then collect answers from several children without immediately saying whether they are right or wrong.

A good way to involve less able members of the class is to demonstrate some of the possible answers by allowing them to be 'Living Numbers'. Have some large cards with numbers, operation signs and equals signs for the children to hold. Ask a number of children to come to the front of the class to illustrate the operation used in working out the problem. Start with a fairly easy one, for example 5p + 5p + 10p = 20p.

Then this maybe?

Games

Have a selection of games for the children to play in pairs or threes. Include sets of bingo cards to help with the learning of addition and multiplication facts and a 'darts' game for adding a series of small numbers mentally.

You could continue playing 'shop' (see page 13) but increase the spending money to 20p.

6 The Treasure Hunt

Programme outline

The Number Crew have organised the animal passengers into two teams to play the 'Number Puzzle' game. The passengers are playing with giant dice which they have to manoeuvre into position so that the spots showing on the two dice add up to four. The presenter talks through the problem and introduces the song 'You've Got to Use Your Brains'.

Flo then introduces the game called 'Difference of Two' where two teams of animals are wearing large numbers and they have to organise themselves into pairs which have a difference of two. Next they all join in the cabin treasure hunt, following the clues that Bradley gives them. Matthew helps viewers with the clues to the treasure trove and introduces the 'Living Numbers' who are trying to find out in how many ways they can make 7 with two dice.

The final challenge is for the viewers to join in the treasure hunt, choose a different cabin number and make up some clues to help friends find the treasure. Or alternatively the viewers can explore ways to make 7 using two dice. The challenge is in fact, using Matthew's words, 'to use their brains!'

Learning outcomes

Children should gain experience of:

● solving numerical problems;

● recognising simple patterns and relationships;

● generalising and making predictions.

Vocabulary

work out	*same way*
calculate	*different way*
answer	*number pairs*
check	

Before viewing

▶ The children should find previous work on number bonds helpful. Have a brief 'warm up' session working orally on number bonds to 10.

While viewing

▶ Stop the tape when Matthew suggests having a go at the Number Puzzle and shows the viewers two fluffy dice. Ask the children to consider what the numbers could be if they have to add to 4.

▶ Help them to sing along with 'You've Got To Use Your Brains' and the title song (see pages 26 and 30).

▶ Stop the tape again and take some time to rehearse the 'Difference of Two' problem.

Follow-up activities

Recap

Discuss the programme with the children. Ask them to describe what happened when the animals played the games.

Sing the song 'You've Got To Use Your Brains' again.

End-of-programme problem

Matthew leaves the children with an invitation 'to use their brains'.

Have some large dice to use when asking the class to think of ways to make 7. (You could make these by putting numbers on large wooden blocks.) Remind the children that they can only use addition and the numbers 1 to 6. Follow this by asking them to think of ways to make 8, 9 and 10. More able children could find ways of making all the numbers up to 12. Ask why there are more ways to make 7 than to make 12 when using two dice.

Not many children know that the spots on opposite faces of a dice add up to 7. Take a large dice and hold it up in front of the class. Do a bit of magic, and then tell the class what number they can see and ask them for the number you can see.

After being introduced in this way to looking at the spots on a dice, children can work in pairs with smaller dice. More able children can be given two dice to work with.

Treasure hunt and 'What number is in my pocket?'

Following the example in the programme, choose a different number and make up clues with the class. For example, the first two clues could be:

There are 20 rooms for you to use.
It's where you go to have a snooze.
The cabin you are looking for
Has just one digit on the door.

You could then ask the children which cabin numbers it could be. The third clue could be:

If the treasure you would see,
An odd number you will need.

You could then ask the children what odd cabin numbers are left. Then give the fourth and final clue:

The number that you want to see
Is less than seven and more than three.

Move on to the game of 'What's the number in my pocket?' giving clues as in the programme but not in rhyme. For example:

Clue 1 The number is less than 20.
Clue 2 It's a 2-digit number.
Clue 3 It's an even number.
Clue 4 It's between 14 and 18.

Make up questions to help the children as you go along.

Give the class a clue, such as 'it's a number under 20', and then the children ask questions to find the number. You can only reply yes or no to their questions. The children may need help making up the most effective questions. To keep track of the numbers which have been eliminated, take the numbers from a number washing line or cross out the relevant numbers on a hundred-square.

Hall games

Similar games to the one above can be played in the hall using large cards or bibs. On instruction, the children have to find a partner to make a total of 7, 8, and so on.

7 | It's Yo-Yo Time

Programme outline

Bradley has discovered a box of yo-yos in the stores and given them to the gorilla to play with. Soon, all the other animals have joined him and gone yo-yo mad. They are playing with the yo-yos all the time. Matthew also takes up yo-yoing and explains what 'all the time' really means. He looks at what people are doing, hour by hour, and he tells us what the different parts of the day are called.

The Number Crew are worried that their passengers will exhaust themselves by constantly playing yo-yo. The crew decide to take turns to watch over them, morning, noon and night. The children share the day watches and Ted watches all night. It is very hard to stop the animal passengers playing with their new toys, but when Baby Bunting has a go with a yo-yo and looks so silly, the craze stops dead in its tracks.

Learning outcomes

Children should gain experience of:

● the vocabulary related to time;

● using units of time appropriately;

● the 24-hour day.

Vocabulary

time	*night*
hours	*noon*
morning	*days of the week*
afternoon	*weekends*
evening	

Before viewing

▶ Talk to the children about different times of day. Ask: What time is midday? Does anyone know what time it would be at midnight? When is bedtime? home time? story time? lunchtime? play time? Which times come before teatime? Which times come after teatime?

▶ Get the children to say what activities they do in the morning. What about in the afternoon? in the evening? in the night?

▶ Have any of the class got yo-yos? What's their favourite time for yo-yoing? (See page 32 for ten yo-yo facts.)

While viewing

▶ Stop the tape when Matthew asks the question: 'What exactly does "all the time" mean?' Talk through the concept of day and night.

▶ Encourage the children to sing along with 'Morning, Afternoon, Evening And Night' and the title song (see pages 29 and 30).

Follow-up activities

Recap

Allow time for the children to tell you about what they have seen and heard. Talk about the number of hours in each day and how the Number Crew split up the 24 hours to make sure there was always someone to look after the animals. Would the class have split the day in this way? Are there other ways to split it up?

Repeat the 'Morning, Afternoon, Evening And Night' song.

End-of-programme problem

Use an analogue clock with movable hands and show the children that the hour hand goes round the clock twice for each full day. Compare with a digital clock if you have one. Talk about the usual 'daily' routine. Talk through the children's school day and what happens in the morning, in the afternoon and when they go home. Order the events of the school day. Make a chart divided into 'morning', 'afternoon', 'evening' and 'night' for Monday to Friday, and list what the children do. Then ask the children: What do you do on the days you do not come to school? Which days are these?

Take up Matthew's challenge and ask the children how to work out how much of their time is spent sleeping, eating, in lessons, and so on. Start the activity with the whole class working out some of the times before asking children to work individually.

Link with science

Talk about the differences between daytime and night-time. What happens to birds and butterflies in the evening? Ask if the children know of any animals that sleep during the day and come out at night. They probably know about pet hamsters or wild animals such as foxes and badgers.

Ask if any of the children have parents who have to work through the night.

Link with literacy

Find stories and poems about time, including days of the week, and encourage the children to learn some traditional rhymes by heart.

After much discussion individual children could then be encouraged to record their daily routine, with your help.

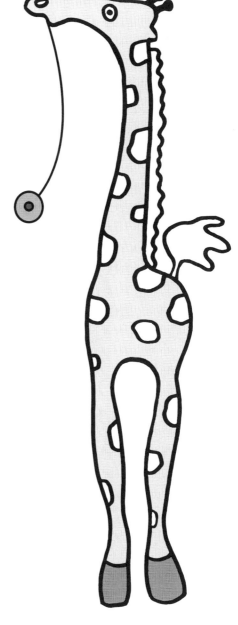

8 | Do it for Charity

Programme outline

The animal passengers decide they would like to do something to help animals less fortunate than themselves, so they decide to do some activities for charity – things like walking, keeping quiet and reading. The Number Crew realise that they will need some clocks to time their passengers' various activities.

Matthew shows an analogue and a digital clock. They look different but both do the same job – tell the time. It depends which one you prefer. He introduces the 'Tell The Time' song. The Number Crew see that digital and analogue clocks look different and begin to learn to read the time on them. Matthew shows that it is an hour between one o'clock and two o'clock. Then he has a quick quiz on how to work out how long certain activities take.

The animal passengers work hard at their activities. Baby Bunting goes in for the 'staying quiet' activity. He falls asleep, so he is quiet for a very long time. He wakes up later, though, and keeps everyone awake all night.

Learning outcomes

Children should gain experience of:

● reading the time from analogue and digital clocks;

● solving problems relating to time.

Vocabulary

clock	stopwatch
hands	hour
how long to go?	seconds
how long will it be until ...?	long time
	short time

Before viewing

▶ Make a display of clocks and timers. Ask if anyone knows the time when school starts in the morning, when they go home, when they go to bed, and so on. Many of them will probably know that twelve o'clock is lunchtime.

While viewing

▶ Stop the tape when Fiz and Bradley realise they have got to learn to tell the time. Ask the children if they can help.

▶ Encourage the children to join in the 'Tell The Time' and title songs (see pages 29 and 30).

Follow-up activities

Recap

Ask the children to think about what they have seen and heard.

Sing the song 'Tell The Time' again.

Talk about what they would regard as a 'long time' or a 'short time'. Does time seem to pass quickly when they are doing something interesting? Does it seem to pass slowly if they are bored?

End-of-programme problem

Talk about activities which last one hour, two hours or three hours. Put up a chart for the three categories and ask children to think of appropriate activities. Children might mention a favourite TV programme, a visit to the cinema, a lesson or a walk in the park. Encourage the children to explain, if they can, how they knew or estimated the time taken for the various activities.

Telling the time during the day

Encourage the children's awareness of the time by having a working clock in the classroom which you refer to naturally during the school day. Encourage regular timings of weather or other scientific observations which can gradually become more accurate over the term. As the children gain confidence, ask them to tell you when it is time for break, nearly time for lunch, and so on. This is a great incentive for them to learn to tell the time accurately.

Quiz game

Have a whole-class session in the form of a quiz. Divide the class into teams and have an analogue clock with movable hands. Ask questions like: What time does this clock show? What time will it be in two hours? This clock shows three o'clock. How many hours to six o'clock? The time is seven o'clock. What time was it two hours ago?

How many hours are there between two o'clock and five o'clock?

Get the children to come to the front of the class and demonstrate, with the clock, how they worked out the answers. Others may be able to write down the calculation. Ask them to come and write it on the board. Follow the whole-class session by getting the children to work in pairs and asking them to make up some time problems for each other.

Analogue and digital clocks

Have a whole-class session with analogue and digital clocks. Make digital time cards from 1:00 to 12:00 and have a large analogue clock with moving hands available. Choose a time card and show it to the class. Get a child to match the digital time with the analogue clock.

9 | Sports Day

Programme outline

Flo and Bradley decide that a sack race would be a good idea for Sports Day and Fiz thinks an egg-and-spoon race would be great. However, when she tries out the idea, the egg ends up all over Bradley. Bradley then has a tough time finding sacks for the animal passengers, until he realises that the four-legged animals need large sacks while the two-legged ones need smaller sacks.

Matthew shows how to sort the passengers into two groups and how to record the information. He helps Fiz to sort her animals for the egg-and-spoon race in the same way. Things get a bit chaotic when both races start at once, but, with an incredible amount of luck and skill, the monkey makes it to the finishing line and wins.

Learning outcomes

Children should gain experience of:

● collecting and recording numerical data.

Vocabulary

large	graph
small	block graph
sort	diagram
order	sorting diagram
match	

Before viewing

The programme will be most effective for children who have had experience of practical sorting activities in real life. Knowing how to sort things can be very useful. For example, sorting a pile of money into different coins helps when you want to find out how much money there is. The children may be able to give other examples of when sorting is useful.

While viewing

▶ Stop the tape when Matthew says the Number Crew need to sort out the animals. Ask the children if they can help.

▶ Encourage the children to sing along with 'If You've Got A Lot Of Animals' and the title song (see page 30).

Follow-up activities

Recap

Discuss the programme with the children, asking them to think about what they have seen and heard.

Repeat the song 'If You've Got A Lot Of Animals'.

Ask questions like: How did Bradley work out how many sacks he needed for his race? How did Fiz work out how many eggs and spoons she needed for her race?

End-of-programme problem

One of Matthew's suggestions is to find out whether there are more boys or girls in the viewers' class. Help the children to make a graph to find out by first asking them to draw a picture of themselves on a small piece of paper. Then, with some guidance, they should place the drawings in the appropriate places on an outline graph you have prepared. If you feel the children know their birthdays, or at least the months of them, the sketches could be used, instead, to find out which month of the year has most birthdays.

A different approach would be to do a 'number' sort. Categories could be odd and even, one-digit numbers, two-digit numbers, numbers which end in 5, and so on. Record your findings on a chart or diagram on the board or flip chart and adjust the level of difficulty to suit the class.

Link with literacy

Use the children's awareness of their names to collect data. Talk about initial letters and the number of letters in each name. Ask questions like: Which names have most letters? How many names begin with D, or H? How many children have names with five letters? Six letters? You could use named drawings of the children, arranging them on a graph or chart.

Link with science

Sorting collections of materials into categories helps children become aware of different materials. Talking to the children about the sorting is essential. Describing the qualities of the materials sorted and counting the number in each category are also meaningful experiences. Help the children to record their findings appropriately.

A project on 'Ourselves' offers many opportunities to sort attributes into categories – eye colour, for example. A simple bar chart can serve as a focus in looking for similarities and differences.
For example: How many children have blue eyes?
How many more children have blue eyes than green eyes? Which eye colour is most common?

Link with geography

Collect class information such as different ways of coming to school, whether the children live in flats, houses or bungalows, and so on. All this information can provide useful material for making graphs.

FINISH

10 | The Number Crew Awards

Programme outline

The Number Crew decide to show some clips of the video tapes that Ted has made during the trip. The deck is decorated and the animal passengers sit at tables while Bradley shows three video clips featuring the following events: 'The Storm and Seasickness', 'The Odd Effect of Orange Juice', and 'Roller Booting'. The animals have to vote for their favourite video using gold blocks. Matthew shows how the blocks can turn into a graph. The animal passengers vote 'The Storm and Seasickness' video clip their favourite.

Flo takes over the microphone to introduce some sporting videos taken on the trip: 'Baby Bunting Bowling', 'Animals Yo-Yoing', and 'The Sports Day Races'. The video clip of the monkey on Sports Day wins.

Matthew shows extracts from three songs, so that the viewers can vote for their favourite song, collect the information and present it in the form of a graph. Then it is time to say 'goodbye' to the Number Crew.

Learning outcomes

Children should gain experience of:

● collecting and recording numerical data;

● making predictions from the data collected.

Vocabulary

graph
block graph
chart

list
most popular
least popular

Before viewing

The programme will be most effective if the children have had some previous experience of organising and presenting data in a variety of ways.

▶ Talk to the children about their favourite television programmes, films, songs from the charts, and so on. How would they like to present this information? Is there a 'best' way?

While viewing

▶ Stop the tape when Bradley asks the passengers to vote. Ask the class to vote, perhaps with a show of hands, on their favourite of the three video clips shown in the programme. See if the children make the same choice as the animal passengers.

▶ Stop the tape again when Flo asks the animal passengers to vote. Again allow the children to vote and compare their choices with those of the animals.

▶ Encourage the children to join in 'When You're Counting', 'There's More Than One Way Of Solving A Problem', 'Mass Mass' and the title song. (See pages 27 and 30. For the words and music of 'When You're Counting', see the **Numbers and the Number System** Teachers' Guide, page 27.)

Follow-up activities

Recap

After the programme, encourage the children to talk about what they have seen and heard. Help the children to describe in their own words what happened in the programme.

Sing the three songs – 'When You're Counting', 'There's More Than One Way Of Solving A Problem', 'Mass Mass' – again.

End-of-programme problem

Write the titles of the three songs on the board and help the children to make a block graph by first asking them to vote for their favourite song. Once the graph has been made, ask questions like:

● How many children voted for each song?

● Which song was the most, or least, popular?

● How many children voted altogether?

● How many more votes does one song have than another?

What questions could the children answer by looking at the graph?

Data handling in other subject areas

Extend the children's experience of making graphs while working on science topics like 'ourselves'. Personal measurements, provided they are dealt with sensitively, can be the source of interesting graph work, as can hair and eye colour. Graph making should be meaningful. Always discuss the graphs with the class when they are complete in order to demonstrate the amount of information you can get from them. Ask the class: How do we know that all the children in the class have been included? What predictions can be made from the graph?

A prediction experiment

Have a bowl of small cubes or beans and ask the children to take a handful and count how many cubes or beans they can hold in their right hand. Make a record of the results. Then ask the children to predict how many they could hold with their left hand. Repeat the experiment and discuss the results.

Song Sheets

Drink Drink

Chris Ellis & Paddy Kingsland

Drink drink drink drink Come try some love - ly

drink You may not like wat - er but real - ly you ought - a It's

love - li - er than you think Come try this con - tain - er no
It's low - er and wid - er it's
If you're not tall or small this con -

need to com - plain for it's big and it's tall and it's high Come
just the right size a con - tain - er that's got what it takes Come
tain - er's for all - you crea - tures of med - i - um size Come

on get your trunk in yes give it a dunk - in This con -
on dip your lip in it's time you were sipp - in It's -
on put your muzzle in it's time you were guzzl - ing As you

1 & 2

tain - er is el - e - phant si - zed!
perf - ect for turt - les and snakes s s s!

3

drink this con - tain - er dry!

You've Got To Use Your Brains

Chris Ellis & Paddy Kingsland

Here's a prob - lem add - ing to four Think of one way think of more Have a

go have a try Have a think what to do You've got to use your brains in the Num - ber Crew!

Here's a problem what do you do?
Make a pair with a difference of two
Have a go have a try have a think what to do
You've got to use your brains in the Number Crew!

Roll those dice around the floor
Seven's what you're looking for
Have a go have a try have a think what to do
You've got to use your brains in the Number Crew!

The cabin you are looking for
Has just one digit on the door
Have a go have a try have a think what to do
You've got to use your brains in the Number Crew!

Mass Mass

Chris Ellis & Paddy Kingsland

Mass mass he's got so much mass As
far as his mass goes he's top of the class
If there is one thing he cer - tain - ly has It's
mass - es and mass - es and mass - es of mass!

Weigh weigh
They've got to be weighed
Who will be heavier
Which one would you say?
If they're on a see-saw
Who goes up or down?
The one with the most mass
Goes down to the ground

There's More Than One Way Of Solving A Problem Chris Ellis & Paddy Kingsland

There's more than one way of solv - ing a prob - lem There are
lots of differ - ent ways that you can choose Think ab - out the ways be - fore you choose one
of them Which - ev - er way you choose it's up to you You can
share or add or take aw - ay To mult - i - ply's an - oth - er way Four
differ - ent ways for an - y - one to choose Yes there are!

Spending twenty p's a very good example
You can start by sharing out what you will spend
Or you can take away the cost of things you sample
Or make a list and add it at the end
You can share or add or take away
To multiply's another way
Four different ways for anyone to choose! Yes there are!

One And Two

Chris Ellis & Paddy Kingsland

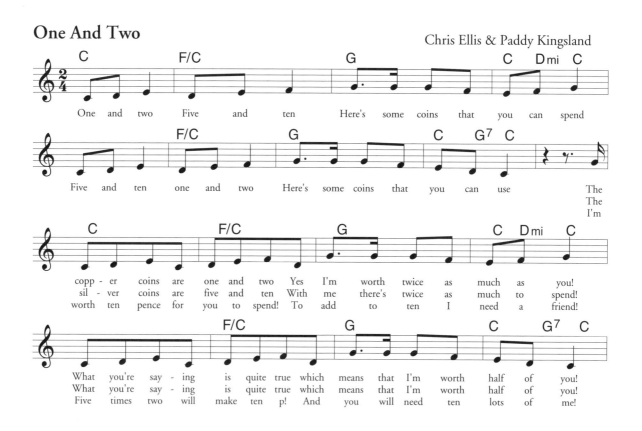

One and two Five and ten Here's some coins that you can spend
Five and ten one and two Here's some coins that you can use The

copp - er coins are one and two Yes I'm worth twice as much as you!
sil - ver coins are five and ten With me there's twice as much to spend!
worth ten pence for you to spend! To add to ten I need a friend!

What you're say - ing is quite true which means that I'm worth half of you!
What you're say - ing is quite true which means that I'm worth half of you!
Five times two will make ten p! And you will need ten lots of me!

It Needs To Be Longer

Chris Ellis & Paddy Kingsland

It needs to be lon - ger tall - er wi - der yes much bigg - er all ar -

ound Or else his bott - om will stick right through and bump al - ong the

ground You don't want the ride to be a sur - prise That brings

tears to your eyes So bett - er make sure he's not on the floor and mea - sure him up for size

It needs to be shorter smaller narrower
Yes much smaller all around
Or else the penguin'll fall about
And she'll be rattled around
You don't want the ride to be a surprise
That brings tears to your eyes
So better make sure she's not on the floor
And measure her up for size

They've got the right length and width and height
So they're the right size all around
And all the animals fit just right
And don't get thrown around
They don't want the ride to be a surprise
That brings tears to their eyes
So better make sure they're not on the floor
And measure them up for size!

Morning, Afternoon, Evening And Night

Chris Ellis & Paddy Kingsland

First thing in the morning they're all performing
Clever tricks with their yo-yos
And the afternoon too that's all that they do
They're always on the go go

The evening's the same they're playing the game
They carry on all through the night
'Cos they can't get enough of this yo-yoing stuff
Morning afternoon evening and night!

Tell The Time

Chris Ellis & Paddy Kingsland

If You've Got A Lot Of Animals

(To a rap rhythm)

If you've got a lot of animals you really need to count
You've got to find an easy way to sort them out
Put all the ones with two legs together in a hoop
And all the ones with four legs should join the other group

You've sorted all the animals you've finished the first half
You want it looking clearer so you've made a graph
Pile the blocks up side by side – a very clever plan
To show the things you've counted just as clearly as you can!

If you've got a lot of animals you really need to count
You've got to find an easy way to sort them out
Put all the bigger ones together in a hoop
And then all the smaller ones go in the other group

You've sorted all the animals you've finished the first half
You want it looking clearer so you've made a graph
Pile the blocks up side by side – a very clever plan
To show the things you've counted just as clearly as you can!

The Number Crew

Chris Ellis & Paddy Kingsland

The King's Bed

A long time ago in a country far away, there lived a King and his Queen who enjoyed giving each other surprise presents. The Queen did not know what to buy the King for his next birthday, which was in three months' time. He had so many fabulous jewels and rich clothes. She found it difficult to think of something new. She thought and she thought. Then she had a brilliant idea. At the court there was a skilled craftsman called Petrusco who made beautiful things. She would ask him to make a special bed for the King's birthday. That would be a real surprise present.

The Queen sent for Petrusco and described what she wanted. 'No problem, Your Majesty,' replied Petrusco. 'You will keep it a secret, won't you?' asked the Queen. 'Of course. I am a person who keeps secrets. I shall have to think how to get the right measurements without the King knowing,' replied Petrusco.

And sure enough he did. Petrusco drew a line on the floor which he thought was about the same height as the King. Then he walked along the line carefully placing one foot after the other. He counted six. So the length of the bed should be six feet. Petrusco estimated how wide the bed should be and drew another line. This time he counted three feet. He ordered the lengths of timber to make a bed six feet long and three feet wide.

Unfortunately, before he could start work on the bed, he had a message from the King. There was some urgent work to be done at one of the other palaces and they must leave immediately. Petrusco went to the Queen and told her of the King's message and explained that he would not be able to make the bed for the King's birthday.

'Of course you will have to go,' said the Queen. 'But I am very disappointed that I shall not be able to give the King his very special birthday present.' Then Petrusco said, 'May I make a suggestion, Your Majesty? Since I have made all the measurements and chosen the most beautiful materials, could I suggest that my son makes the bed? He is still an apprentice but he is a very fine craftsman already and it would mean the King could have his bed for his birthday.'

So the King and Petrusco and the other workmen set off for the distant palace. The King promised he would be back to celebrate his birthday. While the others were away the apprentice looked at his father's drawings and began work on the King's bed. He followed his father's instructions and the King returned the day before his birthday. The bed was just about ready. The Queen had it hidden in a spare room to be shown to the King on his birthday. The King's birthday arrived, and the Queen was very excited when she took the King to the room where his present had been hidden. The King looked at the bed. The workmanship was of the highest quality but there was something wrong.

It was too small.

'It's too small,' said the Queen. 'But Petrusco promised he would take great care with the measurements.' She sent for Petrusco and his son and asked what had gone wrong. 'I do not know,' said the boy. 'I followed my father's instructions exactly. He said the bed should be six feet long and three feet wide. But I can see it is too small for the King. What has happened? I know! My feet are smaller!'

'But it is so beautiful,' said the Queen. 'It will be just right for the Princess.'

'I shall make another bed for Your Majesty,' said Petrusco.

'I think before anyone makes anything else, we should all agree exactly how long a foot is,' said the King. 'I insist that the length of my foot should always be used.' So a law was passed which made the King's foot the standard which everyone should use, to make sure there were no more mistakes in the future.

A rod was made out of brass exactly the same length as the King's foot, and put into a glass case. Pieces of wood were cut to match and when workmen wanted to measure they used the lengths of wood and called the length a 'foot'. And everyone knew they were all using the same foot.

Ten Yo-Yo Facts

The yo-yo has bounced back into fashion in a big way. It's one of the latest crazes to hit the high street, and it's not confined to children. Here are some facts about yo-yos.

Did you know that…?

- The yo-yo is thought to have been around for hundreds or even thousands of years, making it one of the oldest toys in history.

- People are not sure where it came from. A Greek vase from 500 BC shows a young child playing with one. Most people believe that yo-yos came from the Philippines and were used as hunting and war weapons. Hunters hid up in the trees and used rocks tied to string to throw at the wild animals as they passed below them. The rocks would come up again and give the hunters another chance.

- By the seventeenth century yo-yos had spread to Europe. Napoleon, the French emperor, is said to have relaxed by playing with his yo-yo before the battle of Waterloo in 1815. Yo-yos were brought to Britain in the eighteenth century and were called 'bandalopes'.

- No-one is sure where the yo-yo got its name. In 1791 some French people called it 'joujou de Normandie' and in the Philippines the word yo-yo means 'come back again'.

- In 1927, Pedro Flores, an American immigrant from the Philippines, began making and selling yo-yos.

- In 1929 an American called Donald Duncan bought Pedro Flores' company and promoted the toy all over the United States.

- In America, 6 June has been named National Yo-Yo Day in honour of Donald Duncan's birthday.

- The largest yo-yo ever made was 3.17m wide and weighed 407kg. Made by students at Stockport College, it was launched by crane from a height of 57m in 1993 and yo-yoed four times.

- Over 3000 Internet sites have been devoted to the yo-yo.

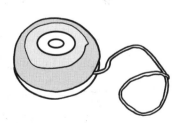

- In 1998, on average, 140 000 yo-yos were sold every week worldwide and the yo-yo market was worth £1 million a month.